Teacher's Resource Masters
Operations and Algebraic Thinking

Daily Common Core Review

Enrichment

Scott Foresman·Addison Wesley

enVisionMATH®
Common Core

PEARSON

Glenview, Illinois • Boston, Massachusetts • Chandler, Arizona • Upper Saddle River, New Jersey

PEARSON

ISBN-13: 978-0-328-68789-3
ISBN-10: 0-328-68789-8

4 5 6 7 8 9 10 V011 15 14 13 12

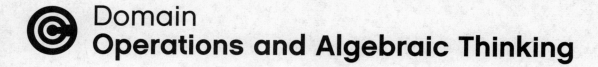

Domain
Operations and Algebraic Thinking

Topic 1	**Multiplication and Division: Meanings and Facts**
Topic 2	**Generate and Analyze Patterns**

Each lesson has a Teacher Resource Master for Daily
Common Core Review, Reteaching, Practice and Enrichment.

Topic 1 **Multiplication and Division: Meanings and Facts**

Topic 2 **Generate and Analyze Patterns**

1. Celia used an addition expression to find 6×5. Which expression did she use?

   A $5 + 5 + 5$

   B $5 + 5 + 5 + 5$

   C $5 + 5 + 5 + 5 + 5 + 5$

   D $5 + 5 + 5 + 5 + 5 + 5 + 5$

2. The Perez family is driving to visit relatives. The trip is 184 miles, and they have driven 48 miles. How many more miles do they need to travel?

   A 142 miles

   B 136 miles

   C 128 miles

   D 112 miles

3. Los Angeles is one of the largest cities in the United States. The population of Houston is less than that of Los Angeles. Chicago has a population greater than Houston but less than Los Angeles. Phoenix has fewer people than Houston. Which lists the population of the cities from greatest to least?

   A Chicago, Los Angeles, Houston, Phoenix

   B Los Angeles, Houston, Phoenix, Chicago

   C Los Angeles, Chicago, Houston, Phoenix

   D Los Angeles, Phoenix, Chicago, Houston

4. What is another way of naming 900?

   A 9 ones

   B 9 tens

   C 9 hundreds

   D 9 thousands

5. Order the numbers from least to greatest.

   852   528   582

   _____

6. Compare. Use $<$, $>$, or $=$.

   329 _____ 785

7. **Mental Math** Una put the same number of carnations into 4 vases. If she used a total of 32 carnations, how many are in each vase?

   _____

   _____

   _____

8. Look for a pattern and write the missing numbers.

   2, 8, 14, 20, 26,

   ____, ____, ____

Meanings of Multiplication

There are 4 rows of 5.

Addition sentence:

5 + 5 + 5 + 5 = 20

Multiplication sentence:

4 × 5 = 20

There are 3 boxes. There are 7 books in each box.

There are 3 groups of 7.

Addition sentence:

7 + 7 + 7 = 21

Multiplication sentence:

3 × 7 = 21

Write an addition sentence and a multiplication sentence for each picture.

1. 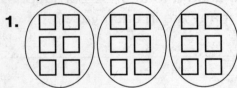 _____

2.  _____

Write a multiplication sentence for each addition sentence.

3. 10 + 10 + 10 + 10 = 40 _____

4. 3 + 3 + 3 + 3 + 3 + 3 = 18 _____

5. Number Sense Explain how multiplication can help you find 7 + 7 + 7.

_____

Name _____

Meanings of Multiplication

Write an addition sentence and a multiplication sentence for the picture.

1.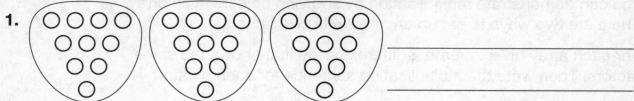

_____

_____

Write a multiplication sentence for each addition sentence.

2. $4 + 4 + 4 + 4 = 16$ _____

3. $10 + 10 + 10 + 10 + 10 + 10 = 60$ _____

4. **Number Sense** How could you use multiplication to find $7 + 7 + 7$?

_____

5. A classroom desk has 4 legs. How many legs do
   5 desks have altogether?   _____

6. Danielle planted 3 seeds in each of 6 different pots.
   How many seeds did she plant?   _____

7. Which is the multiplication sentence for $2 + 2 + 2 + 2$?

   A $4 \times 4 = 16$

   B $2 \times 2 = 4$

   C $4 \times 2 = 8$

   D $2 \times 6 = 12$

8. **Writing to Explain** Explain how you can use multiplication
   to find $2 + 2 + 2 + 2$.

_____

_____

_____

Hurray Array!

You can demonstrate multiplication by showing objects in an array. There are two ways to set up an array with two factors.

For each array given, create a different array that shows the same factors. Then write the multiplication sentence for each picture.

1. ○ ○ ○ ○ ○ ○
   ○ ○ ○ ○ ○ ○ =
   ○ ○ ○ ○ ○ ○
   ○ ○ ○ ○ ○ ○   _____

                                    _____

2. □ □ □ □ □ □   _____
   □ □ □ □ □ □ =
   □ □ □ □ □ □   _____

There are at least two arrays for any product: the number × 1 and 1 × the number. Sometimes there are other possible arrays for a product.

3. Draw the other array for the product 25.
   Write the multiplication sentence.

   _____

4. Draw the other array for the product 9.
   Write the multiplication sentence.

   _____

Sometimes there are several different arrays that can be drawn for a product.

5. Draw an array for the product 28 that is not 28 × 1, 1 × 28, 7 × 4, or 4 × 7. Write the multiplication sentence for your array.

   _____

Name _____

1. What is seven hundred one written in standard form?

   A 17

   B 71

   C 107

   D 701

2. The Electronic Experts store sold 812 computers last year. The store also sold 233 printers. How many computers and printers did the store sell last year?

   A 1,045

   B 1,025

   C 945

   D 645

3. Georgia made $123 mowing lawns over the past four weeks. Sidney made $96 mowing lawns over the same amount of time. How much money did they make altogether?

   A $219

   B $223

   C $239

   D $242

4. Which numbers are written in order from least to greatest?

   A 423, 415, 430, 402

   B 430, 423, 415, 402

   C 415, 402, 430, 423

   D 402, 415, 423, 430

5. Ike wanted to run 900 laps around a track in three months. Ike has already run 438 laps. How many more laps does he have left to meet his goal?

   _____

6. Look for a pattern. Write the next three numbers.

   5, 9, 13, 17, ____, ____, ____

7. Carol, Ana, Gloria, and Luz are standing in a line. Gloria is first. Luz is not last and is ahead of Carol. Ana is behind Gloria and Carol. In what order are the girls in line?

   _____

   _____

8. **Mental Math** James has 8 model cars. Rita and James have 17 model cars all together. How many model cars does Rita have?

   _____

   _____

Name _____

Patterns for Facts

Pattern   **Example**

All multiples of two are even numbers.   2, 18, 44

All multiples of 5 end in 0 or 5.   25, 100, 220

For all multiples of nine, the sum of   27 $2 + 7 = 9$
the digits is always a multiple of 9.   63 $6 + 3 = 9$

1. $\begin{array}{r} 9 \\ \times\ 5 \\ \hline \end{array}$	**2.** $\begin{array}{r} 2 \\ \times\ 8 \\ \hline \end{array}$	**3.** $\begin{array}{r} 5 \\ \times\ 8 \\ \hline \end{array}$	**4.** $\begin{array}{r} 9 \\ \times\ 4 \\ \hline \end{array}$
5. $\begin{array}{r} 9 \\ \times\ 3 \\ \hline \end{array}$	**6.** $\begin{array}{r} 2 \\ \times\ 7 \\ \hline \end{array}$	**7.** $\begin{array}{r} 5 \\ \times\ 3 \\ \hline \end{array}$	**8.** $\begin{array}{r} 5 \\ \times\ 6 \\ \hline \end{array}$
9. $\begin{array}{r} 9 \\ \times\ 2 \\ \hline \end{array}$	**10.** $\begin{array}{r} 5 \\ \times\ 7 \\ \hline \end{array}$	**11.** $\begin{array}{r} 6 \\ \times\ 3 \\ \hline \end{array}$	**12.** $\begin{array}{r} 2 \\ \times\ 6 \\ \hline \end{array}$

13. How many baseball cards are
in 4 packages?

_____

Item	Number in Package
Baseball cards	5
Stickers	2
Coupons	9

14. How many stickers do you
get if you buy 9 packages?

_____

15. How many coupons do you get if you buy
7 packages?

_____

Name _____

Patterns for Facts

1.   5
   × 4
   ‾‾‾‾

2.   2
   × 3
   ‾‾‾‾

3.   9
   × 7
   ‾‾‾‾

4.   5
   × 2
   ‾‾‾‾

5.   8
   × 2
   ‾‾‾‾

6.   5
   × 3
   ‾‾‾‾

7.   9
   × 8
   ‾‾‾‾

8.   9
   × 4
   ‾‾‾‾

9. $9 \times 6 =$ _____

10. $2 \times 7 =$ _____

11. $5 \times 5 =$ _____

Algebra Find the missing number.

12. _____ $\times 9 = 45$

13. $2 \times$ _____ $= 14$

14. A package of baseball cards includes
5 cards. How many baseball cards are
in 5 packages?

_____

15. What is the value of the missing number?
$9 \times \boxed{} = 36$

A 6   **B** 4   **C** 3   **D** 2

16. Writing to Explain Milton needs to find the product of two
numbers. One of the numbers is 9. The answer also needs to
be 9. How will he solve this problem? Explain.

_____

_____

_____

Patterns, Patterns Everywhere

Complete each pattern and write the rule for the pattern you find.
Hint: The pattern may involve more than one operation.
For example, the numbers 2, 4, 16, 32, 128 form a pattern of
multiplying by 2, then multiplying by 4.

Pattern Rule

1. 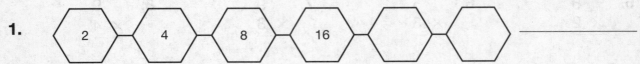 2 4 8 16 _____

2. 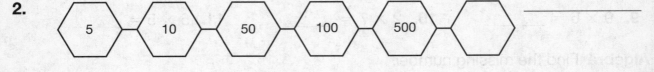 5 10 50 100 500 _____

3. 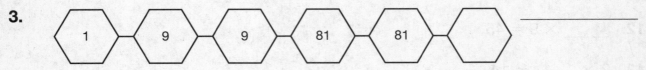 1 9 9 81 81 _____

4. 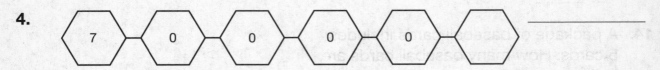 7 0 0 0 0 _____

5. 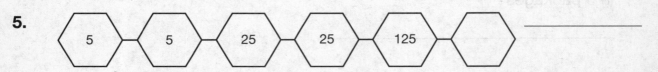 5 5 25 25 125 _____

6. 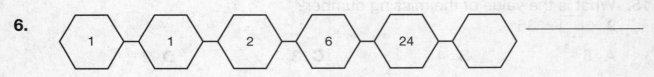 1 1 2 6 24 _____

7. Although a single starfish may have as many as 44 arms,
we are most familiar with starfish that have 5 arms. Write a
number pattern for 6 starfish if each had 5 arms. How many
arms would those starfish have in all?

_____

_____

1. **Estimation** Ronni estimated the sum of 149 and 863 by rounding each number to the nearest hundred and then adding. What was Ronni's estimate for 149 + 863?

   A 1,100

   B 1,000

   C 900

   D 700

2. A grocery store had 176 cans of green beans on the shelf on Monday. By Friday, 37 cans had been sold. How many cans were left?

   A 127

   B 139

   C 143

   D 151

3. A page in a photo album holds 6 pictures. A photographer fills 9 pages with pictures. How many pictures were put in the album?

   A 15

   B 45

   C 54

   D 72

4. There are 6 rows of desks in a classroom, and 4 desks per row. How many seats are there in all?

   A 2

   B 10

   C 18

   D 24

5. Write a number pattern for 8 starfish if each had 5 arms.

   _____

   _____

6. What number do the place-value blocks below show?

   _____

7. **Mental Math** Kyle counted 7 windows on the first row of a building that has 5 floors. Each floor has the same number of windows. How many windows does the building have?

   _____

8. The printer sent 150 newspapers for delivery one day. How many boxes of newspapers would there be if the newspapers were packed in tens?

   _____

   _____

Name _____

Multiplication Properties

You can use the Properties of Multiplication to help you find products.

Commutative Property of Multiplication

You can multiply any two numbers in any order.

$2 \times 3 = 3 \times 2$

Identity Property of Multiplication

When you multiply any number by 1, the product is that number.

$7 \times 1 = 7$

Zero Property of Multiplication

When you multiply any number by 0, the product is also 0.

$3 \times 0 = 0$

---

1. $7 \times 3 = 3 \times$ _____

2. $4 \times 0 =$ _____

3. $5 \times 4 = 4 \times$ _____

4. $2 \times 1 =$ _____

5. $0 \times 7 =$ _____

6. $8 \times 3 = 3 \times$ _____

7. $9 \times 1 = 1 \times$ _____

8. $1 \times 5 =$ _____

9. Number Sense How do you know that $35 \times 5 = 5 \times 35$ without finding products?

_____

_____

_____

10. Writing to Explain Explain how you know that in
? $\times 6,273 = 6,273$, the ? will be 1.

_____

Name _____

Multiplication Properties

1.
$$\begin{array}{r} 0 \\ \times\ 4 \\ \hline \end{array}$$

2.
$$\begin{array}{r} 1 \\ \times\ 3 \\ \hline \end{array}$$

3.
$$\begin{array}{r} 7 \\ \times\ 1 \\ \hline \end{array}$$

4.
$$\begin{array}{r} 5 \\ \times\ 0 \\ \hline \end{array}$$

5.
$$\begin{array}{r} 1 \\ \times\ 8 \\ \hline \end{array}$$

6.
$$\begin{array}{r} 3 \\ \times\ 0 \\ \hline \end{array}$$

7.
$$\begin{array}{r} 4 \\ \times\ 1 \\ \hline \end{array}$$

8.
$$\begin{array}{r} 6 \\ \times\ 0 \\ \hline \end{array}$$

9. $1 \times 1 =$ _____

10. $9 \times 0 =$ _____

11. $0 \times 0 =$ _____

Algebra Find the missing number. Tell which property can help you.

12. _____ $\times\ 3 = 0$

13. $1 \times$ _____ $= 4$

_____

_____

14. Ray has 4 boxes with 5 pens in each box. Kevin has 5 boxes with 4 pens in each. Who has more pens?

_____

15. Which property can help you find the missing number? _____ $\times\ 6 = 0$

_____

16. **Writing to Explain** Milton needs to find the product of two numbers. One of the numbers is 6. The answer also needs to be 6. How will you solve this problem? Explain.

_____

_____

_____

How Does Your Garden Grow?

Area is the name for the number of square units that are in a given space. You can figure out the area of a rectangle as you would an array. You can also break apart a rectangle to form different combinations and still have the same area.

Here is Mary's garden: 4 × 6 = 24 square units.

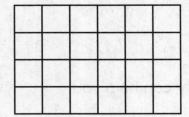

Draw lines and write the first letter of the flower to show several possible planting plans.

1.

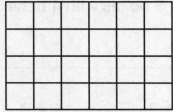

2 × 6 = tulips
2 × 4 = roses
2 × 2 = marigolds

2.

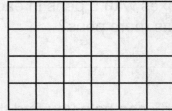

4 × 4 = tulips
2 × 2 = roses
2 × 2 = marigolds

3.

3 × 4 = tulips
1 × 6 = roses
3 × 2 = marigolds

4.

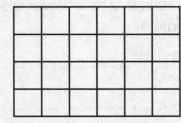

4 × 5 = tulips
3 × 1 = roses
1 × 1 = marigolds

1. Which is the missing number?
$(7 \times 2) + (7 \times 6) = 7 \times \boxed{}$

   A 8

   B 6

   C 4

   D 2

2. **Mental Math** What number can go in the box to make the equation true? $6 \times \boxed{} = 48$

   A 5

   B 6

   C 7

   D 8

3. Which of the following is used to find out how many inches there are in 4 feet?

   A $4 + 12$

   B 4×12

   C $12 - 4$

   D $12 \div 4$

4. A restaurant cuts its large pizzas into 8 equal pieces. How many total pieces of pizza are in 9 pizzas?

   A 72

   B 60

   C 45

   D 27

5. Compare. Use $<$, $>$, or $=$.
846 $\bigcirc$ 824

   _____

6. If Curtis walked 3 miles each day for 26 weeks, how many miles will Curtis have walked?

   _____

7. How many equal sides does a square have?

   _____

8. Write the word form for this number and give the value of the underlined digit.
9<u>8</u>2

   _____

   _____

   _____

3, 4, 6, 7, and 8 as Factors

You can use breaking apart to help find the product.

Example How many baseball cards do you have if you have 4 packages with 6 cards in each package?

You need to find 4×6.

4 groups of 6 are the same as 4 groups of 3 plus 4 groups of 3.

$4 \times 3 = 12$

$4 \times 3 = 12$

$4 \times 6 = (4 \times 3) + (4 \times 3)$

$\quad = 12 + 12$

$\quad = 24$

You have 24 baseball cards.

Use breaking apart to find each product.

1. $3 \times 5 =$ _____

2. $9 \times 4 =$ _____

3. $6 \times 6 =$ _____

4. $3 \times 7 =$ _____

5. $5 \times 7 =$ _____

6. $8 \times 4 =$ _____

7. $6 \times 7 =$ _____

8. $7 \times 8 =$ _____

Compare. Use $<$, $>$, or $=$ to fill in each $\bigcirc$.

9. $7 \times 4 \bigcirc 7 \times 5$

10. $6 \times 6 \bigcirc 3 \times 7$

11. $8 \times 3 \bigcirc 3 \times 8$

12. $9 \times 5 \bigcirc 12 \times 3$

13. Number Sense Explain how 9×4 can help you find 9×8.

_____

_____

_____

3, 4, 6, 7, and 8 as Factors

For **1** through **8**, fill in each ____.

1. $3 \times 10 = (2 \times 10) + (1 \times$ ____$)$

2. $2 \times$ ____ $= (2 \times 5) + (2 \times 1)$

3. $4 \times 7 = (4 \times$ ____$) + (4 \times 2)$

4. $11 \times 8 = (11 \times 5) + (11 \times$ ____$)$

5. $3 \times 6 = (3 \times 1) + (3 \times$ ____$)$

6. $6 \times 6 = (6 \times$ ____$) + (6 \times 4)$

7. $7 \times$ ____ $= (7 \times 4) + (7 \times 3)$

8. $1 \times 8 = (1 \times$ ____$) + (1 \times 3)$

For **9** through **20**, use breaking apart to find each product.

9. 5×5 ____

10. 3×6 ____

11. 4×2 ____

12. 7×3 ____

13. 7×2 ____

14. 6×6 ____

15. 7×7 ____

16. 6×7 ____

17. 8×3 ____

18. 10×6 ____

19. 6×12 ____

20. 4×6 ____

For **21** through **29**, compare using $<$, $>$, or $=$ to fill in each $\bigcirc$.

21. $3 \times 4 \bigcirc 6 \times 1$

22. $5 \times 8 \bigcirc 6 \times 7$

23. $3 \times 6 \bigcirc 9 \times 2$

24. $8 \times 4 \bigcirc 7 \times 4$

25. $7 \times 5 \bigcirc 12 \times 3$

26. $5 \times 6 \bigcirc 3 \times 10$

27. $1 \times 8 \bigcirc 2 \times 3$

28. $4 \times 5 \bigcirc 2 \times 10$

29. $8 \times 6 \bigcirc 7 \times 7$

30. Candice has placed her seashells into 4 rows with 5 seashells in each row. How many seashells does she have? ____

31. A chessboard has 8 rows and 8 columns. Each row has 4 white squares and 4 black squares. Which expression below would give you the number of black squares on a chessboard?

  A 8×8 **B** 8×4 **C** 4×4 **D** $8 + 8$

32. **Writing to Explain** Using the breaking apart method, what is the best way to multiply 8 by 7?

_____

Name _____

Moonbeam Multiplication

Earth is not the only planet that has a moon. Most of the other planets in our solar system also have moons. In many cases, they have more than one moon.

1. In 1610, Galileo discovered 4 moons orbiting Jupiter. By 1979, scientists had discovered that Jupiter has 4 times as many moons as Galileo saw. How many known moons did Jupiter have in 1979? _____

2. Mars has 2 known moons. By 1990, Saturn was known to have 9 times as many moons as Mars. How many known moons did Saturn have in 1990? _____

3. Until 1989, scientists had discovered only 2 moons of Neptune. Since then, scientists have found 4 times as many moons orbiting Neptune as they originally thought. How many known moons does Neptune have? _____

4. By 1999, Uranus was known to have 21 times as many moons as Earth. How many known moons did Uranus have in 1999? _____

5. Suppose you go to soccer practice 5 days a week. How many days would you go to practice in 4 weeks? _____

6. Suppose you work on homework 2 hours a day. How many hours would you work in 5 days? _____

7. A magazine costs $3.00. How much would you pay for 6 magazines? _____

8. A tray of muffins contains 2 cups of blueberries. How many cups of blueberries are in 3 trays? _____

1. Daryl is 23 years old. His brother Larry is 11 years younger. Which number sentence can you use to find how old Larry is?

   A $23 - 11 = 12$

   B $23 + 11 = 34$

   C $34 - 23 = 11$

   D $23 - 12 = 11$

2. Donna has read 9 times as many pages as Bob has. Bob has read 8 pages. How many pages has Donna read?

   A 17

   B 54

   C 72

   D 81

3. Raja put 35 marbles into a jar. Mary put in 28 marbles. Sal put in 64 marbles. What is the order from least to greatest, based on the amount of marbles each person put in the jar?

   A Mary, Raja, Sal

   B Sal, Mary, Raja

   C Sal, Raja, Mary

   D Raja, Mary, Sal

4. **Estimation** Dennis has 171 shells in his collection. Fred has 208. Round each amount to the nearest ten. About how many more shells does Fred have?

   _____

5. Marissa has 10 grapes. Roger has 3 times as many grapes as Marissa has. How many grapes do Marissa and Roger have in all?

   _____

6. Ian multiplied a number by 5. He then multiplied that product by 2. What digit is in the ones place of the final product?

   _____

Problem Solving: Look for a Pattern

What pattern do you see?

1 A 2 B 3 C 4 D 5 E 6 F

The numbers alternate with letters of the alphabet, in order.
The pattern would continue like this:

7 G 8 H 9 I

What pattern do you see?

A	B	C
1	1	1
2	2	4
3	3	9
4	4	16
5		25

The number in column A is multiplied by the number in column B.
Column C is the product.

The last number in column B would be 5.

Look for a pattern. Draw the next two shapes.

1.

Look for a pattern. Write the three missing numbers.

2. 2, 4, 6, 8, _____ , _____ , _____

3. 2, 7, 12, 17, _____ , _____ , _____

4. 60, 52, 44, 36, _____ , _____ , _____

5. 88, 77, 66, 55, _____ , _____ , _____

Problem Solving: Look for a Pattern

Look for a pattern. Draw the next two shapes.

1.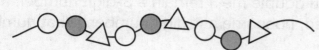

2.

Look for a pattern. Write the missing numbers.

3. 5, 8, 11, 14, 17, _____ , _____

4. 4, 6, 10, 16, 24, _____ , _____

Look for a pattern. Complete each number sentence.

5. $80 + 8 = 88$

   $800 + 88 = 888$

   $8,000 + 888 =$ _____

   $80,000 + 8,888 =$ _____

6. $10 + 1 = 11$

   $100 + 1 = 101$

   $1,000 + 1 =$ _____

   $10,000 + 1 =$ _____

Look for a pattern. Write the missing numbers.

7. Sally went to purchase tiles for her kitchen floor. She measured the floor to find how many tiles she needed to cover the floor. Sally decided to make a pattern. She chose 10 red tiles,

   20 beige tiles, 30 white tiles, _____ black tiles, and _____ gray tiles to complete a pattern for the kitchen floor.

8. **Reasoning** Fill in the missing amounts to update Carl's savings passbook.

Carl's Savings Account		
Date	Deposit	Balance
4/7	$25	$945
4/14		$995
4/21	$25	
4/30	$50	
5/7		$1,095

What Number Am I?

Identify each number based on the information in
each paragraph.

1. I am a 3-digit whole number. If you double me, I remain a 3-digit number. If
you add 2 to me after I am doubled, I become a 4-digit number. What number
am I?

_____

_____

2. I am a 4-digit whole number. My digits decrease by 2 from the thousands place
to the ones place. Each of my digits is an even number. What number am I?

_____

_____

3. I am a whole number. When you add 3 to me you get a 2-digit number.
That 2-digit number is the same as 3 four times. What number am I?

_____

_____

4. I am a number less than 10. When I am divided by 2, half of that number is
also 2. What number am I?

_____

_____

1. Melissa has 19 more stamps than George. If George has 24 stamps, how many stamps does Melissa have?

   A 33

   B 39

   C 43

   D 45

2. **Mental Math** Madison's hair was 10 inches long before she got it cut. She had 3 inches cut off. How many inches long is her hair now?

   A 3 inches

   B 6 inches

   C 7 inches

   D 13 inches

3. Timothy gave a clerk a $20 bill for a book. The clerk gave him back $11 in change. How much did the book cost?

   A $10

   B $9

   C $8

   D $7

4. **Mental Math** Andrew, Lynda, and Fiona each have 9 marbles. How many marbles do they have all together?

   _____

5. Miguel is putting his books away on a bookcase. There are 5 shelves on the bookcase. Miguel has 30 books. How many books should Miguel put on each shelf so that each shelf has an equal number of books?

   _____

6. Tamika had $15 to spend at the fair. She played a game for $2, rode on the Ferris wheel for $3, and bought a sandwich for $4. How much money did she have left?

   _____

Meanings of Division

When you divide, you separate things into equal groups.

Doris is making 8 box lunches, each with the same number of strawberries. She has a total of 32 strawberries. How many strawberries should go in each lunch?

What you think: Doris will have to place an equal number of strawberries in each box. She must put 32 strawberries into 8 equal groups. How many strawberries are in each group?

What you show: 8 equal groups

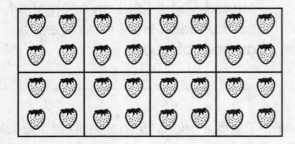

32 strawberries divided into 8 separate groups leaves 4 strawberries in each group.

What you write: 32 ÷ 8 = 4

32 is the dividend, the number that is being divided.

8 is the divisor, the number the dividend is being divided by.

4 is the quotient, or the answer to the division problem.

Each lunch should have 4 strawberries.

Draw pictures to solve each problem.

1. You put 15 marbles into 3 groups.
   How many marbles are in each group?

_____

2. You need to put 20 ice cubes into
   5 glasses. How many cubes
   should go into each glass?

_____

Meanings of Division

Draw pictures to solve each problem.

1. There are 12 small gift bags. Each bag can hold 1 toy and some stickers. There are 36 stickers. If an equal number of stickers is put in each bag, how many stickers will be in each bag?

   _____

2. One egg carton holds 12 eggs. How many cartons are you able to fill with 60 eggs?

   _____

3. There are 21 students in Mr. Tentler's class. The students divided themselves evenly into 3 groups. How many students are in each group?

   _____

4. Calvin read an 18-page chapter in his social studies book in 2 hours. If he read the same number of pages each hour, how many pages did he read per hour?

   A 3 pages   **B** 6 pages   **C** 9 pages   **D** 12 pages

5. **Writing to Explain** A class is planning a party. A pizza restaurant cuts each pizza into 8 slices. There are 32 students. How many pizzas does the class need to order for each student to have a slice? Explain.

   _____

   _____

   _____

Baby-Sitting in the Neighborhood

Jennifer baby-sits for some of the families in her neighborhood. She wants to decide how she can earn the most money. She has made a chart that shows how long she usually baby-sits for a family and how much she is paid for her job.

Family	Hours	Amount Paid
Roberts	6	$30
Robinsons	6	$24
San Giacomos	8	$40
Lings	5	$35
Oberlins	7	$42

1. Which family pays the most per hour? What is the hourly rate?

_____

2. Which family pays the least per hour?

_____

3. Which would pay more, 8 hours of baby-sitting for the Oberlins or 7 hours of baby-sitting for the San Giacomos?

_____

_____

4. On one Friday night, Jennifer is asked to baby-sit for two different families. The Robinsons need her for 5 hours, and the Lings want her to baby-sit for 4 hours. If Jennifer can only take one job and wants to make the most money, which job should she take? How much will she earn?

_____

5. On a different Friday night, the Roberts offer Jennifer a 5-hour baby-sitting job with a $4 tip, and the Robinsons offer Jennifer an 8-hour baby-sitting job. Which job should Jennifer take? How much more will she earn?

_____

1. **Mental Math** Alexandra has 12 flowers. She puts the same number of flowers in each of her vases. How many flowers will be in each vase?

   A 3
   B 4
   C 8
   D 12

2. Look at the array below. Which multiplication sentence describes the array?

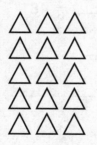

   A 3 × 3 = 9
   B 5 × 3 = 15
   C 3 × 6 = 18
   D 5 × 5 = 25

3. **Mental Math** Keith planted 45 carrots in his garden. He planted them in 5 rows. Each row had the same number of carrot plants. How many carrot plants were in each row?

   A 3
   B 5
   C 9
   D 15

4. Jackson wants to buy a pair of sneakers that cost $106. So far, he has saved $57. How much more does Jackson have to save to buy the sneakers?

_____

5. Put the numbers in order from least to greatest.

   352   253   325   532

_____

6. Michelle wrote a basic multiplication fact, but she covered up some of the numbers. What multiplication fact did she write?

   [   ] × [   ] = 25

_____

Relating Multiplication and Division

Multiplication and division are related, just like addition and subtraction are related.

This is the fact family for 5, 6, and 30:

$5 \times 6 = 30$	$30 \div 6 = 5$
$6 \times 5 = 30$	$30 \div 5 = 6$

Complete each fact family.

1. $2 \times$ _____ $= 10$

_____ $\times$ _____ $= 10$

$10 \div 5 =$ _____

$10 \div$ _____ $=$ _____

2. $9 \times$ _____ $= 27$

_____ $\times$ _____ $= 27$

$27 \div 3 =$ _____

$27 \div$ _____ $=$ _____

3. $8 \times$ _____ $= 72$

_____ $\times$ _____ $= 72$

$72 \div 8 =$ _____

$72 \div$ _____ $=$ _____

4. $6 \times$ _____ $= 48$

_____ $\times$ _____ $= 48$

$48 \div 8 =$ _____

$48 \div$ _____ $=$ _____

Write a fact family for each set of numbers.

5. 7, 4, 28

_____

6. 5, 8, 40

_____

7. Number Sense What multiplication facts are part of the fact family for $12 \div 3 = 4$?

_____

Relating Multiplication and Division

Complete each fact family.

1. $7 \times$ _____ $= 42$

    _____ $\times$ _____ $= 42$

    $42 \div 6 =$ _____

    $42 \div$ _____ $=$ _____

2. $9 \times$ _____ $= 36$

    _____ $\times$ _____ $= 36$

    $36 \div 4 =$ _____

    $36 \div$ _____ $=$ _____

Write a fact family for each set of numbers.

3. 6, 3, 18

_____

4. 5, 5, 25

_____

5. Reasoning Why does the fact family for 81 and 9 have only two number sentences?

_____

_____

_____

6. Which number sentence completes the fact family?

    $9 \times 6 = 54$ $54 \div 9 = 6$ $54 \div 6 = 9$

    A $9 \times 9 = 81$ **B** $6 \times 9 = 54$ **C** $6 \times 6 = 36$ **D** $8 \times 6 = 48$

7. Writing to Explain Find two ways to divide 16 evenly. Explain.

_____

_____

Just the Facts

Write each missing number. Then, write a related
multiplication fact.

	Missing Number	Related Fact
1. $27 \div 3 =$	_____	_____
2. $48 \div 6 =$	_____	_____
3. $32 \div 8 =$	_____	_____
4. $18 \div 3 =$	_____	_____
5. $63 \div 9 =$	_____	_____

Choose from the missing numbers you found above to make
these sentences true.

6. There are _____ pints in 3 quarts.

7. There are _____ legs on an octopus.

8. There are _____ days in a week.

9. A baseball game lasts _____ innings.

10. A dog has _____ legs.

1. Last year, there were 420 students at Madison Elementary. This year, 190 more students enrolled. How many students attend Madison Elementary now?

   A 230

   B 380

   C 510

   D 610

2. There were 213 people in the audience at Erika's recital. Twenty-nine were children. How many adults were at the recital?

   A 184

   B 204

   C 232

   D 242

3. **Estimation** To visit his grandmother, James' family drove 309 miles and then stopped to have lunch. The entire trip is 589 miles. About how many more miles does James' family have left to drive?

   A 300 miles

   B 200 miles

   C 150 miles

   D 100 miles

4. Find the missing digits in the problem below. Rewrite the subtraction sentence.

   ```
     917
   − 2??
     705
   ```

   _____

Use the table for problems **5** and **6**.

Number of Books Read	
Class 4A	875
Class 4B	750
Class 4C	925

5. The fourth-grade students at Milton Elementary kept track of the number of books they read. Which class read the greatest number of books?

   _____

6. How many more books did Class 4A read than Class 4B?

   _____

Special Quotients

There are special rules for dividing numbers by 1 and by 0.

Rule: A number divided by 1 is that number.

Examples: $4 \div 1 = 4$ $55 \div 1 = 55$

Rule: A number divided by itself (except 0) is 1.

Examples: $17 \div 17 = 1$ $135 \div 135 = 1$

Rule: Zero divided by a number (except 0) is 0.

Examples: $0 \div 4 = 0$ $0 \div 15 = 0$

Rule: You cannot divide a number by zero.

Examples: $7 \div 0$ cannot be done $12 \div 0$ cannot be done

---

1. $0 \div 2 = $ _____   **2.** $4 \div 4 = $ _____

3. $0 \div 7 = $ _____   **4.** $9 \div 9 = $ _____

5. $0 \div 3 = $ _____   **6.** $10 \div 10 = $ _____

7. $0 \div 11 = $ _____   **8.** $11 \div 1 = $ _____

Compare. Use >, <, or = for each $\bigcirc$.

9. $6 \div 6 \bigcirc 3 \div 3$ **10.** $7 \div 1 \bigcirc 8 \div 8$

11. $0 \div 5 \bigcirc 3 \div 1$ **12.** $0 \div 4 \bigcirc 0 \div 9$

13. $5 \div 5 \bigcirc 0 \div 5$ **14.** $7 \div 7 \bigcirc 9 \div 9$

15. $8 \div 1 \bigcirc 0 \div 8$ **16.** $9 \div 9 \bigcirc 9 \div 1$

17. $0 \div 12 \bigcirc 12 \div 1$ **18.** $0 \div 11 \bigcirc 0 \div 15$

19. Number Sense If $a \div 4 = 0$, what do you
know about a?   _____

Special Quotients

1. $0 \div 10 =$ _____

2. $7 \div 1 =$ _____

3. $8 \div 8 =$ _____

4. $9 \div 9 =$ _____

5. $0 \div 5 =$ _____

6. $5 \div 1 =$ _____

7. $1\overline{)4}$ _____

8. $8\overline{)0}$ _____

9. $3\overline{)3}$ _____

10. $1\overline{)6}$ _____

11. **Number Sense** If $x \div 9 = 1$, how do you know what x is? Explain.

_____

_____

12. Kenneth has 22 math problems to do for homework. He has 12 problems done. How many more problems does he have left? If he completes 1 problem every minute, how many more minutes does he have to work?

_____

13. There are 8 people who would like to share a box of granola bars that contains 8 bars. How many granola bars does each person get if they share equally?

_____

14. Which is the quotient of $20 \div 20$?

    A 20   **B** 2   **C** 1   **D** 0

15. **Writing to Explain** Write the rule that applies to the following number sentence: $0 \div 7 = 0$.

_____

_____

_____

Analogies

An analogy is often used to show the relationship between pairs of items.

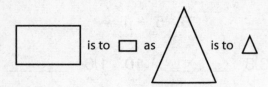

1. How are the drawings of the rectangles related?

   _____

   _____

2. How are the drawings of the triangles related?

   _____

   _____

3. Draw the missing item in the following analogies.

   a. is to as is to _____

   b. 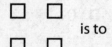 is to _____ as is to

   c. _____ is to as is to

   d. is to as _____ is to

1. Elizabeth is baking cookies for her birthday party. She has invited 12 people to her party. She wants each guest to have 2 cookies. How many cookies does she need to bake for her guests?

   A 20

   B 22

   C 24

   D 26

2. There were 32 students going on a field trip. Each van could carry 8 students. Which number sentence is in the same fact family as $32 \div 8 = \square$?

   A $4 \times \square = 32$

   B $32 \times 8 = \square$

   C $\square \times 4 = 8$

   D $8 \times 8 = \square$

3. **Mental Math** In which number sentence does 5 make the equation true?

   A $3 \times 2 = \square$

   B $\square \times 6 = 42$

   C $9 \times \square = 45$

   D $\square \times 3 = 18$

4. Complete the fact family below.

   $4 \times \underline{\hspace{1cm}} = 20$

   $\underline{\hspace{1cm}} \times 4 = 20$

   $\underline{\hspace{1cm}} \div 5 = 4$

   $20 \div \underline{\hspace{1cm}} = 5$

5. Complete the fact family below.

   $\underline{\hspace{1cm}} \times 6 = 42$

   $\underline{\hspace{1cm}} \times 7 = 42$

   $42 \div 7 = \underline{\hspace{1cm}}$

   $\underline{\hspace{1cm}} \div 6 = 7$

6. Arthur, Jorge, and Dylan collected 328 cans for recycling all together. Arthur collected 105 and Jorge collected 112. How many did Dylan collect?

   _____

Using Multiplication Facts to Find Division Facts

Tile Floor Darren is laying a tile floor in the hallway. The pattern for the floor is shown to the right.

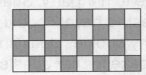

First, use Darren's tile floor to write a multiplication story for $4 \times 8 = 32$.

> Darren's tile floor has 4 rows with 8 pieces of tile in each row. How many pieces of tile are there in all?

Second, use Darren's tile floor to write a division story for $32 \div 4 = 8$.

> Darren has 32 small triangles. He needs 4 for each shaded square. How many shaded squares can he make with the small triangles?

Use the data in the table to write a multiplication or a division story for each number fact. Solve.

Building Supplies	Number in a Box
Fasteners	6
Bolts	12

1. 6×4

_____

_____

_____

2. $12 \div 4$

_____

_____

_____

Using Multiplication Facts to Find Division Facts

Solve.

1. $12 \div 3 =$ _____

2. $20 \div 5 =$ _____

3. $50 \div 10 =$ _____

4. $27 \div 9 =$ _____

5. $6 \div 2 =$ _____

6. $16 \div 8 =$ _____

7. $63 \div 9 =$ _____

8. $36 \div 4 =$ _____

9. $48 \div 6 =$ _____

10. $32 \div 8 =$ _____

11. $25 \div 5 =$ _____

12. $18 \div 2 =$ _____

Use the data in the table to write a multiplication story for the number fact. Solve.

First Aid Kit	
Supply	**Number in Kit**
Bandages	4
Cleanser Pads	6
Cotton Balls	12

13. $2 \times 6 =$

_____

_____

14. Which is the quotient of $28 \div 7$?

A 14   **B** 9   **C** 6   **D** 4

15. Writing to Explain Write a division story for 12 and 3.

_____

_____

_____

Name _____

Table That Rule

Below are some tables. Dewey, Corrie, and Isaac each try to guess the rule. If the rule is correct, write **yes.** If the rule is incorrect, write the correct rule. Complete each table.

1. Dewey says, "The rule for this table is divide by 4."

Dewey's Table	16	32	56	48	12	18	24	30	n
	8	16	28						

_____

_____

2. Corrie says, "The rule for this table is multiply by 2, then subtract 1."

Corrie's Table	7	2	6	4	12	3	10	5	11	n
	13	3	11							

_____

_____

3. Isaac says, "The rule for this table is add 1."

Isaac's Table	2	9	6	4	3	5	8	7	9	n
	3	24	15	9						

_____

_____

Name _____

1. Which of the following has a 9 in the hundreds place?

   A 199

   B 259

   C 392

   D 923

2. Yvette's computer has a folder with files shown in rows and columns. There are 4 rows and 8 columns. Which number sentence shows how many files the folder has?

   A $4 \times 8 = 32$

   B $8 - 4 = 4$

   C $4 + 8 = 12$

   D $8 \div 4 = 2$

3. Nick has 700 baseball cards. He gives 374 to his younger sister. How many baseball cards does Nick have now?

   A 226

   B 276

   C 326

   D 436

4. What kind of figure has 3 sides?

   A Square

   B Triangle

   C Pentagon

   D Trapezoid

5. What fraction of the triangles is shaded?

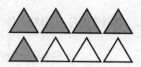

   A $\frac{1}{2}$

   B $\frac{3}{8}$

   C $\frac{5}{8}$

   D $\frac{6}{8}$

6. Nina has 465 pennies in a jar. Daryl has 348 pennies in a jar. How many pennies do they have all together?

   _____

7. The table shows how many marbles four friends have in their collections. Write the amounts in order from greatest to least.

   _____

   Marble Collections

Person	Number
Sven	580
Rita	572
Wendy	610
Carlos	602

Problem Solving: Draw a Picture and Write an Equation

Draw a picture and write an equation.

Step 1:
Read and Understand

Janie is in the fourth row of the marching band. There are 7 rows of musicians with 8 in each row. How many musicians are ahead of Janie? How many musicians are behind Janie?

You need to find how many are ahead of Janie and behind Janie.

Step 2:
Plan and Solve

You can draw a picture of the musicians: Write an A for each musician ahead of Janie, a B for each musician behind Janie, and a J for each musician in Janie's row.

Solve

A A A A A A A A ⎫
A A A A A A A A ⎬ 24
A A A A A A A A ⎭
J J J J J J J J } 8
B B B B B B B B ⎫
B B B B B B B B ⎬ 24
B B B B B B B B ⎭

Step 3:
Look Back and Check

How many musicians are there ahead of Janie? You can multiply.
3 × 8 = 24

There are 24 musicians ahead of Janie.

How many musicians are behind Janie? You can multiply.
3 × 8 = 24

There are 24 musicians behind Janie.

1. James has 12 seashells mounted in a row. The 6 shells in the center of the row are nautilus shells. Is there the same number of shells on either side of the nautilus shells? Draw a picture to help you solve the problem.

_____

_____

Name _____

Problem Solving: Draw a Picture and Write an Equation

For **1** through **4**, write an equation and solve. Use the picture to help.

1. John is running in a race. The race is 25 miles long. After two hours, John has run 7 miles. How many miles does John have left to run?

2. A summer camp has divided its campers into 8 groups of 9 campers. How many campers are at the summer camp?

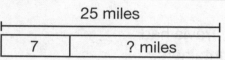

25 miles	
7	? miles

? campers							
9	9	9	9	9	9	9	9

3. Karen is 5 feet tall. In Karen's backyard there is an oak tree 4 times as tall as she is. How tall is the oak tree?

4. Micah's room has four sides and a perimeter of 48 feet. If 3 of the sides are 12 feet long, how long is the fourth side?

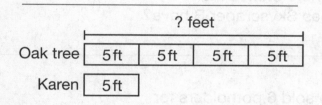

	? feet			
Oak tree	5 ft	5 ft	5 ft	5 ft
Karen	5 ft			

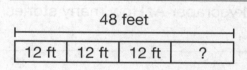

48 feet			
12 ft	12 ft	12 ft	?

5. On Monday, Chris had $250 in his savings account. On Friday, he spent $16 at the movies. On Saturday, he deposited a $120 check. Which number sentence below shows how much money Chris has?

A 250 + 16 + 120

C 250 − 16 − 120

B 250 + 16 − 120

D 250 − 16 + 120

6. Melissa is making bookmarks from a piece of ribbon that is 12 inches long. Each bookmark is 4 inches long. She drew this picture to see how many bookmarks she could make from the ribbon. What did she do wrong?

12 inches in all			
4 inches	4 inches	4 inches	4 inches

Picture It!

Draw pictures or bar diagrams to help you solve the problems below.

1. Mr. Byfield and Ms. Fuentes each have 18 students in their classes. Half of the students in Mr. Byfield's class are girls. There are 2 more girls in Ms. Fuentes' class than in Mr. Byfield's. How many girls are in Ms. Fuentes' class?

   _____

2. There are 8 small containers of milk in a case. Travis had 5 cases of milk in his store. He sold 2 small containers. How many containers does Travis have now?

   _____

3. A hotel is 7 stories high. Skyscraper A has 28 more stories than the hotel. Skyscraper B has 3 more stories than Skyscraper A. How many stories does Skyscraper B have?

   _____

4. At the fourth-grade craft sale, Karen sold 6 potholders for $4 each. Larry made $5 more than Karen selling bookmarks. How much did Larry make?

   _____

Name _____

Choose the best answer.

1. José has 22 marbles and 2 jars. He places the same number of marbles in each jar. How many marbles are in each jar?

   A 11

   B 20

   C 24

   D 44

2. Which fraction below has a different value from the others?

$$\frac{1}{2}, \frac{1}{3}, \frac{3}{6}, \frac{4}{8}$$

   A $\frac{1}{2}$

   B $\frac{1}{3}$

   C $\frac{3}{6}$

   D $\frac{4}{8}$

3. There are 10 years in a decade. How many decades are there in 90 years?

   A 9

   B 8

   C 7

   D 6

4. Of the 28 students in Ms. Marsh's class, 15 walk to school. How many of the students find some other way to get to school?

   A 43

   B 33

   C 13

   D 3

5. Mental Math Which number makes both number sentences true?

$$56 \div \boxed{} = 8$$

$$8 \times \boxed{} = 56$$

6. Tim needs 18 pens. He can buy them in packages of 6, 9, or 12. He will buy only one type of package. Which packages could Tim buy? Write two different ways that Tim could buy exactly 18 pens.

_____

_____

_____

_____

7. A group of 9 people spent $78 to go to the movies. Adult tickets cost $10 each and student tickets cost $8 each. How many adult tickets were purchased?

_____

D 2·1

Name _____

Repeating Patterns

Patterns can grow or patterns can repeat.
Repeating patterns can use numbers or shapes.
You can extend a pattern by finding a rule for the pattern.

Repeating Patterns with Shapes

Use this pattern.
What is the next shape?

Assign each shape a number. When a shape repeats use the same number.

1 2 3 1 2 3 1

The next shape is the second shape.

Repeating Patterns with Numbers

Use the pattern below. What is the 12th number in this pattern?

4, 7, 3, 5, 4, 7, 3, 5, 4, 7, ...

Find the pattern.
The pattern is 4, 7, 3, 5, and then it repeats.

Extend the pattern until reaching the 12th number.

4, 7, 3, 5, 4, 7, 3, 5, 4, 7, 3, 5

The 12th number is 5.

---

1. Draw the next three shapes in the pattern.

_____

2. What are the next three numbers in the pattern below?
5, 8, 3, 1, 5, 8, 3, 1, 5, 8

_____

3. Explain It In the pattern in Exercise 2, how could you find the 15th number? What is that number?

_____

_____

_____

Repeating Patterns

Draw the next three shapes to continue the pattern.

1.

_____

2.

_____

Write the next three numbers to continue the pattern.

3. 4, 6, 2, 8, 4, 6, 2, 8, 4, …

_____

4. 3, 3, 5, 3, 3, 5, 3, 3, 5, …

_____

5. **Draw a Picture** What is the 12th shape in the pattern below?

_____

6. **Strategy Practice** Penny has made a pattern of shapes on her bedroom walls. She drew a rectangle, 2 circles, a rectangle, and then 2 more circles until she drew 24 circles. How many shapes did she draw in all?

_____

7. Mrs. Washington placed students in a line. The order was 1 boy, 2 girls, 2 boys, and continued. Was the 10th student a boy or a girl?

_____

8. What is the 15th number in the pattern below?
3, 6, 5, 2, 3, 6, 5, 2, …

A 2　　　　　**B** 3　　　　　**C** 5　　　　　**D** 6

Name _____

Line Patterns

Find the pattern in each group of lines.
Then draw the next three lines to continue the pattern.

1.

2.

3.

4.

5.

6.

Choose the best answer.

1. While on vacation, Ming collected 8 stones from the beach. She sorted her stones by color. The table below shows Ming's stone collection.

Ming's Stone Collection

Color	White	Brown	Yellow	Blue
Number	2	1	3	2

What fraction of Ming's collection is yellow?

A $\frac{1}{6}$ C $\frac{3}{8}$

B $\frac{1}{3}$ D $\frac{1}{4}$

2. David's bowling scores are shown in the table below.

Bowling Scores

Game	Score
1	175
2	137
3	146

What was David's score for these 3 games?

A 358 C 457

B 447 D 458

3. Which is an example of the Associative Property of Addition?

A $4 + 7 = 7 + 4$

B $(3 + 9) + 6 = 3 + (9 + 6)$

C $8 + 0 = 8$

D $9 + 5 = 7 + 7$

4. Five friends played ring toss at the school fair. Bill went first. Marlene went after Tony. Jill went before Tony. If Jamal went last, who went second?

_____

5. What is the tenth number in the pattern below?
2, 5, 8, 2, 5, 8, …

_____

6. Draw a figure that shows $\frac{1}{4}$ shaded.

7. **Mental Math** Brad waited on 20 customers in 4 hours. He waited on the same number of customers each hour. How many customers did he wait on each hour?

_____

Name _____

Number Sequences

A number sequence is a pattern that increases or decreases while following a rule.

What are the next three numbers in this pattern?

36, 42, 48, 54, …

Step 1	**Step 2**
Find the pattern.	Use this rule to extend the pattern.
You can subtract to find the pattern.	Start with 54. Add 6.
$54 - 48 = 6$	$54 + 6 = 60$
$48 - 42 = 6$	$60 + 6 = 66$
$42 - 36 = 6$	$66 + 6 = 72$
Each number is 6 more than the number before it. So, a rule for the pattern is "add 6."	So, the next three numbers are 60, 66, and 72.

Find the next three numbers in each pattern.
Write a rule for the pattern.

1. 35, 40, 45, ■, ■, ■   **2.** 43, 39, 35, ■, ■, ■   **3.** 32, 39, 46, ■, ■, ■

_____   _____   _____

4. 13, 21, 29, ■, ■, ■   **5.** 75, 65, 55, ■, ■, ■   **6.** 51, 45, 39, ■, ■, ■

_____   _____   _____

7. Critical Thinking How can you use subtraction to complete an addition pattern? Use Exercise 3 as an example.

_____

_____

_____

Name _____

Number Sequences

Find the missing numbers in each pattern. Write a rule for the pattern.

1. 19, 23, 27, ■, ■

_____

2. 32, 26, 20, ■, ■

_____

3. 125, 150, 175, ■, ■

_____

4. 8, 15, ■, ■, 36

_____

5. 90, 80 ■, ■, 50

_____

6. 84, 69, 54, ■, ■

_____

7. 30, 50, ■, 90, ■

_____

8. 65, 56, ■, 38, ■

_____

9. 35, ■, 57, 68, ■

_____

10. Reasoning The house numbers on Carr Memorial Avenue follow a pattern. The first four houses on the left side of the street are numbered 8, 14, 20, and 26. How many more houses are on the left side of the street with numbers less than 50?

_____

11. Noreen is beginning an exercise program. The first week she exercises 25 minutes each day. The second week she exercises 30 minutes a day and the third week she increases it to 35 minutes a day. If the pattern continues, how long will she exercise each day in the fifth week?

_____

12. Explain It What do you need to do to extend a number pattern?

_____

_____

_____

13. John said that 52 is part of the pattern below.
Mary said that 66 is part of the pattern below.
Who is correct?
18, 26, 34, 42, ...

A Neither is correct.

B Both are correct.

C Only John is correct.

D Only Mary is correct.

Name _____

Square Sequences

For **1–10**, find the pattern and fill in the missing numbers.

1. 9 — 18 — 27 — ☐ — ☐ — ☐ — ☐

2. 1 — 4 — 9 — 16 — ☐ — ☐ — ☐

3. 72 — 64 — 56 — 48 — ☐ — ☐ — ☐

4. 42 — 37 — 32 — 27 — ☐ — ☐ — ☐

5. 1 — 3 — 6 — 10 — ☐ — ☐ — ☐

6. 1 — 1 — 2 — 3 — 5 — ☐ — ☐ — ☐

7. 99 — 92 — 85 — 78 — 71 — ☐ — ☐ — ☐

8. 28 — 3 — 31 — 5 — 36 — ☐ — ☐ — ☐

9. 1 — 10 — 2 — 20 — 3 — ☐ — ☐ — ☐

10. 2 — 4 — 3 — 9 — 4 — ☐ — ☐ — ☐

Name _____

Choose the best answer.

1. There are 21 students in one class and 19 in another. The lab has 34 computers. How many students will need to share a computer when both classes are in the lab at the same time?

   A 12

   B 9

   C 7

   D 6

2. **Mental Math** Keira runs 8 blocks every day. What is the total number of blocks Keira runs in a week?

   A 56

   B 49

   C 42

   D 15

3. What is the next number in the pattern below?
   63, 52, 41, 30, _____

   A 29

   B 21

   C 19

   D 11

4. Find the product.

$$\begin{array}{r} 9 \\ \times\ 8 \\ \hline \end{array}$$

5. Warren has $726 in his savings account. He wants to buy a bicycle that costs $348. If he buys the bike, how much money will be left in his savings account?

   _____

6. What fraction of the figure is shaded?

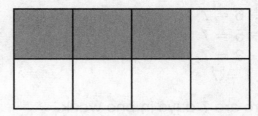

   _____

7. What is a rule for the pattern below?
   9, 16, 23, 30, …

   _____

8. **Mental Math** There are 8 people in each cleanup group. A total of 72 people will participate in the cleanup. How many groups are there?

   _____

Extending Tables

A table is an organized way to show a pattern.

Weeks	Days
1	7
3	21
5	35
6	42
8	?

Each pair of values follows some rule. If you can find a rule that works for all the pairs, you can extend the table.

What is the missing number in this table?

Step 1

Find a rule for the pattern.

The first 4 weeks are shown.
You can divide to find the pattern.

$42 \div 6 = 7$
$35 \div 5 = 7$
$21 \div 3 = 7$
$7 \div 1 = 7$

There are 7 days in one week.

Step 2

Use your rule to find the missing number.

Multiply the days in 1 week by the number of weeks.

$8 \times 7 = 56$

The missing number is 56.

Complete each table.

1.

Cars	Wheels
1	4
2	8
3	
4	16
8	32

2.

Old Price	New Price
$63	$53
$48	$38
	$31
$37	$27
$26	$16

3.

Weight of Salad in Ounces	6	10	14	18
Total Weight of Container in Ounces	9	13	17	

Extending Tables

Find the missing numbers.

1.

Number of Cats	Number of Legs
1	4
2	
3	12
4	16
	32

2.

Money Earned	Money Saved
$25	$15
$32	$22
$43	
	$47
$73	$63

3.

Touchdowns	Points
1	6
2	12
3	
	36
8	48

For **4** and **5**, use the table at the right.

T-shirts	Cost
1	$8
3	$24
5	$40

4. How much money would 9 T-shirts cost?

_____

5. Strategy Practice How much more money do 10 T-shirts cost than 6 T-shirts? Explain how you found your answer.

_____

_____

_____

6. Number Sense Bob has 3 bookshelves that hold a total of 27 books. He adds a fourth shelf and now has 36 books. If he adds 2 more shelves, how many books can he have in total?

_____

7. What is the missing number in the table below?

In	3	5	8	15
Out	9	11	14	

A 21   **B** 25   **C** 30   **D** 45

Right Answer, Write Rule

1. Ashley has 1 teaspoon to measure 5 tablespoons.
If 1 tablespoon is equal to 3 teaspoons, how many
teaspoons does she need?

_____

Complete the table.

Number of Tablespoons	1	2	3	4	5
Number of Teaspoons	3				

Write a rule for the pattern.

_____

_____

2. A rule for this table is "add 7."

Which number does not belong?
What is the correct number?

Mike's Age	Lauren's Age
2	9
5	12
7	15

_____

_____

3. José and his dad went to an aquarium and saw
a tank with 5 octopuses. José counted 8 tentacles
on 1 octopus. Tentacles are like long arms. How
many tentacles do 5 octopuses have? Write a rule. _____

_____

_____

Name _____

Choose the best answer.

1. What is the missing number in the table below?

Hands	Fingers
2	10
4	20
6	
8	40

A 22

B 28

C 30

D 32

2. What are the next three numbers in the pattern below?

7, 9, 3, 1, 7, 9, 3, 1, ____, ____, ____

A 9, 3, 1

B 7, 9, 1

C 7, 9, 3

D 3, 7, 9

3. Bill has 4 letter blocks: *A, B, C,* and *D.* In how many different ways can Bill arrange the blocks in a row?

A 6

B 12

C 18

D 24

4. Compare. Use $<$, $>$, or $=$.

$\frac{3}{8}$ ◯ $\frac{3}{4}$

5. Mandy, Brandy, and Sandy all went out for ice cream. They ordered vanilla, chocolate, and strawberry. Each girl ordered 1 flavor.

• Mandy did not order vanilla.

• Sandy did not order chocolate.

• Brandy always orders strawberry.

Who ordered each flavor?

_____

_____

_____

6. Mental Math Find the product.

$8 \times 11 = \boxed{}$

7. What is the next number in the pattern below?

3, 6, 9, 12, _____

Writing Rules for Situations

When working with tables, it is important to find a rule that works for all pairs of numbers. The rule tells how to find one of the numbers in a pair.

Old Price	New Price
$15	$10
$22	$17
$28	$23
$37	$32
$51	$46

Each pair of numbers in the table to the left follows a rule. If you can find a rule that works, you can extend the table.

Step 1

Find the pattern. Check the first pair of numbers to see how the first number changed to become the second number.

$15 - 10 = 5$

A rule for the first pair of numbers is "subtract 5."

Step 2

See if this rule works for all the values.

$22 - 17 = 5$ $37 - 32 = 5$

$28 - 23 = 5$ $51 - 46 = 5$

The rule "subtract 5" works for every pair of values.

Find the missing numbers in each table. Write a rule for the table.

1.

Earned	Spent
$21	$14
$30	$23
$42	
$48	$41
$59	

2.

Teams	Players
3	27
8	72
6	
9	
2	18

3.

Tickets	Cost
2	$1
6	$3
12	
10	$5
20	

_____   _____   _____

4. **Number Sense** Joe said that by using the information in Exercise 2 there would be 250 players if there were 25 teams. Is that correct? Explain.

_____

_____

R 2·4

Writing Rules for Situations

Find the missing numbers in each table.
Write a rule for the table.

1.

Max's Age	Carol's Age
7	13
10	
14	20
18	24
	31

2.

Tricycles	Wheels
5	15
3	9
7	
	27
2	6

3.

Old Price	New Price
$25	$18
$16	$9
	$32
$53	$46
$72	

_____   _____   _____

For **4** and **5**, use the table at the right.

Players	Teams
24	4
48	8
36	6
30	5

4. The table shows the number of players on a volleyball team. What is a rule for the table?

_____

5. Explain It If there are 12 teams, how many players will there be? Explain how you found your answer.

_____

_____

6. How many miles can Nick travel in 5 hours? 6 hours?

Hours	1	2	3	4
Miles	60	120	180	240

_____

7. The table shows how many CDs Jim and Ken each own after joining a CD club. Which is a rule that works for this table?

Jim	8	12	20	30
Ken	16	20	28	38

A Add 8   **C** Subtract 10

B Multiply by 2   **D** Divide by 2

Name _____

Number Patterns

The students at Parker Elementary School raised money to help pay for new musical instruments. The music store where they purchased the instruments donated $10 for every $1 that the students raised. The students' goal was to raise $700. Complete the chart and use it to answer the questions below.

Group	Week 1	Week 2	Week 3	Week 4	Week 5
Students	$10	$20	$25	$15	$5
Music Store					

1. How many weeks did it take the students to reach their goal? _____

2. At the end of 5 weeks, how much money did the students raise? _____

3. How much did the music store donate in total? _____

4. How much money, including the donations from the music store, was raised altogether after 5 weeks? _____

5. Make a new chart to show how the students could have raised $700 in 3 weeks by changing the amounts raised in the first and second weeks.

Choose the best answer.

1. For an exercise program, Sheila
jogs 35 minutes on Monday,
40 minutes on Tuesday, 45 minutes
on Wednesday, and 50 minutes on
Thursday. If the pattern continues,
how many minutes will she jog on
Saturday?

A 55 minutes

B 65 minutes

C 60 minutes

D 45 minutes

2. **Estimation** Gerry sold 43 energy-
saving light bulbs for a fund raiser.
Mindy sold 78 energy-saving light
bulbs. About how many more
energy-saving light bulbs did
Mindy sell?

A 20

B 25

C 30

D 40

3. There are 12 eggs in one dozen.
How many eggs are there in
8 dozen?

A 80

B 84

C 92

D 96

4. The table shows the number of
points scored in each quarter.

Points Scored by Quarter

Quarter	Points Scored
First	3
Second	7
Third	10
Fourth	8

Complete the bar graph.

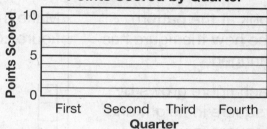

Points Scored by Quarter

5. **Mental Math** It takes 48 minutes
for Mickey to walk 6 laps around
the park. How many minutes does
it take Mickey to walk 1 lap?

_____

Geometric Patterns

Like number patterns, geometric patterns can have figures that grow. To extend geometric patterns follow the same steps as you would for number patterns.

Below is a pattern of squares.

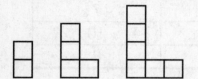

Number of Figure	1	2	3	4	5
Number of Squares	2	4	6		

Step 1

Look at the pattern. See how the figure has changed.

Each figure grows by 1 square in height and 1 square in width.

Each figure grows by 2 squares.

Step 2

Make the next two figures.

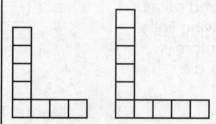

Step 3

Fill in the table.

Number of Figure	1	2	3	4	5
Number of Squares	2	4	6	8	10

Draw the next two towers in the pattern. Use grid paper. Find the missing numbers in each table.

1.

Number of Stories	1	2	3	4	5
Number of Blocks	4	8	12		

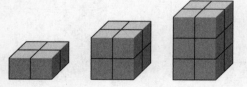

2.

Length of Sides	1	2	3	4	5
Sum of All Sides	5	10	15		

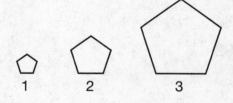

3. **Number Sense** If there were 10 stories in Exercise 1, how many blocks would there be? Explain.

_____

Geometric Patterns

Draw the next two figures in the pattern.
Find the missing numbers in each table.

1.

Number of Stories	1	2	3	4	5
Number of Blocks	5	10	15		

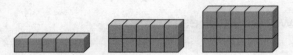

2.

Number of Stories	1	2	3	4	5
Number of Blocks	2	4	6		

3.

Length of Each Side	1	2	3	4	5
Sum of All Sides	3	6	9		

△ △ △
1   2   3

4.

Number of Stories	1	2	3	4	5
Number of Blocks	6	12	18		

5. Explain It Use Exercise 4. How could you find how many blocks there were in 20 stories? How many blocks would there be?

_____

_____

_____

6. Which is a rule for the table below?

In	3	9	4	7
Out	7	13	8	11

A Add 4

B Multiply 2

C Multiply 4

D Add 5

Name _____

Pattern Teasers

Below is a pattern made of cubes called "garages."

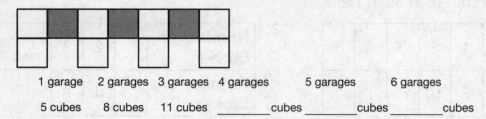

1 garage	2 garages	3 garages	4 garages	5 garages	6 garages
5 cubes	8 cubes	11 cubes	_____ cubes	_____ cubes	_____ cubes

1. Continue the pattern for 6 garages. How many cubes
   were used?   _____

2. How many cubes would be used to make 10 garages? _____

3. Write an expression for the number of cubes for any number
   of garages. Use *n* to stand for any number.

   _____

Here is a number pattern called "bull's eye." Use the pattern for **4** and **5**.

2	2	4	2	4	6
10	12	2	4	6	2
8	8	10	12	8	4
6	6	16	14	10	6
4	4	2	14	12	8
2	10	8	6	4	2

4. Start with the 2 in the upper left-hand corner. Draw a straight
   line across the first 3 numbers, 2, 2, 4. Continue the line
   across the next three numbers, 2, 4, 6. Now, draw a line
   down from the 6. What are the next 4 numbers?

   _____

5. Draw one continuous line that crosses each number only once to complete
   the pattern. Why do you think "bull's eye" is the name for this pattern?

   _____

Name _____

Choose the best answer.

1. How many small squares are in the next figure in the pattern below?

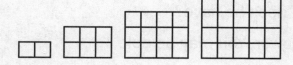

    A 24

    B 30

    C 36

    D 40

2. Ben cut his peanut butter and jelly sandwich into four equal pieces. He ate one piece. What is the fraction of the sandwich that Ben ate?

    A $\frac{3}{4}$

    B $\frac{1}{2}$

    C $\frac{1}{4}$

    D $\frac{1}{8}$

3. Which of the following activities will take about one hour to finish?

    A Jumping into a pool

    B Listening to an entire CD

    C Driving across Texas

    D Reading a sentence of a book

4. Compare $<$, $>$, or $=$.

$\frac{1}{4}$ ◯ $\frac{3}{8}$

5. Kristen scored four 3-point field goals, two 2-point field goals, and seven free throws. Free throws are worth 1 point each. How many points did Kristen score?

_____

6. What is a rule for the table below?

Teams	Players
2	12
5	30
8	48
12	72

_____

7. Use the Associative Property of Multiplication to find this product.
$8 \times 5 \times 2$

_____

Problem Solving: Act It Out and Use Reasoning

Izzie has 12 coins. Four of the coins are quarters. He has 2 more dimes than nickels. How many of each coin does he have?

You can use logical reasoning to find the answer. You may be able to determine information that is not told.

What do I know?	What do I need to find out?	What can I determine from the information?
Izzie has 12 coins. 4 of the coins are quarters. Izzie has 2 more dimes than nickels.	How many dimes does Izzie have? How many nickels does Izzie have?	If 4 of the 12 coins are quarters, Izzie has a total of 8 dimes and nickels.

You can act it out to find how many dimes and nickels Izzie has.

Take 8 two-color counters. Find combinations so that one color will have 2 more than the other. If you try 4 and 4, the difference is 0, so try 5 and 3. It works.

So, Izzie has 4 quarters, 5 dimes, and 3 nickels.

Solve. Find the number of each kind of object in the collection.

1. **Kim's Music Video Collection**

   13 videos in all
   4 concert videos
   3 more rap videos than pop videos

   Concert videos = ☐

   Rap videos = ☐

   Pop videos = ☐

2. **Molly's Art Collection**

   5 paintings
   3 more sculptures than mosaics
   16 pieces in all

   Paintings = ☐

   Sculptures = ☐

   Mosaics = ☐

Problem Solving: Act It Out and Use Reasoning

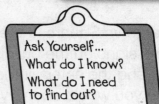

Ask Yourself...
What do I know?
What do I need
to find out?

Solve. Find the number of each kind of object in
the collection.

1. Sue's Card Collection

8 packs of baseball cards
3 fewer packs of hockey cards
than football cards
17 packs in all

Baseball cards = ☐

Hockey cards = ☐

Football cards = ☐

2. Drew's DVD Collection

7 comedy DVDs
4 more drama DVDs than horror
DVDs
15 DVDs in all

Comedy DVDs = ☐

Drama DVDs = ☐

Horror DVDs = ☐

3. Strategy Practice Mike is 8 years
older than Kyle. Kyle is 6 years
old. The sum of Mike's, Kyle's,
and Jamal's ages is 23. How many
years old is Jamal?

_____

4. Miranda has 24 CDs in her
collection. Of those CDs, 10 are
pop CDs. She has 6 more country
CDs than jazz CDs. How many
country CDs does Miranda have?

_____

5. Curt has 12 models in all. Three of the models are airplanes.
Curt has 5 more models of cars than boats. How many
models of cars does Curt have?

_____

6. Stevie, Lindsey, and Christine are the lead singers in a band.
They will sing 18 songs. Lindsey will sing 8 songs. Christine
will sing 6 fewer songs than Stevie. How many songs will
Stevie sing?

A 2   **B** 4   **C** 6   **D** 8

Town Square

In the Geotown Square, there are several shops and entertainment areas. The signs on the buildings show the prices of items you can purchase and the entertainment you can choose. For each exercise, write how you would spend your money and tell how much money you have left. Make sure you do not spend more than you have!

1. You have one $5 bill, three $1 bills, 6 quarters, 3 dimes.

_____

_____

2. You have one $10 bill, 4 nickels, and 7 pennies.

_____

_____

3. You have two $5 bills, two $1 bills, 3 quarters, 1 dime, and 3 nickels.

_____

_____

4. You have fifteen $1 bills, 16 quarters, and 10 dimes.

_____

_____